TOPSY AND TIM
CAN
MAKE MUSIC

Jean and Gareth Adamson

BLACKIE: GLASGOW AND LONDON

Copyright © 1982 Jean and Gareth Adamson

British Library Cataloguing in Publication Data
Adamson, Jean
Topsy and Tim can make music. — (Topsy and Tim
activity books)
I. Title   II. Adamson, Gareth
823'.914[J]   PZ7

ISBN 0–216–91175–3
ISBN 0–216–91174–5   (Pbk)

Blackie and Son Limited
Bishopbriggs, Glasgow G64 2NZ
Furnival House, 14/18 High Holborn, London WC1V 6BX

Printed and bound in Great Britain by
Robert MacLehose & Co. Ltd., Renfrew, Scotland

A car full of grown-ups came to
Topsy and Tim's school. They
carried funny-looking cases.
"Here are the musicians," said Miss
Terry. "They have come to play
for us."

The musicians took their instruments out of the cases. They showed the children how the instruments worked. Then they played lovely music, all together. "You may play music like that one day," Miss Terry told the children, when the concert was over.

"I can play the drum already," said Tim.

Topsy and Tim had their own concert
after tea. Stevie and Tony came too.
Tim found a big, old, empty suitcase.
He whacked it with the hearthbrush.
It made a loud drum.
Topsy whacked a tin tray with a ladle.
Tony bashed two saucepan lids together.
Stevie made trumpet-noises through
a plastic funnel.

Baby Robin Rupert, next door, woke up
and howled.

Mummy came running to see
what the noise was.
"It's our concert," Tim
explained.
"That is a good idea," said
Mummy, "but you mustn't
just make a noise."

Mummy showed them how to make music together in time.
They clapped hands slowly . . . then quickly . . .. then they
clapped to tunes. They soon learnt to clap all together.

Here are some
musical drums
that Mummy found
in the kitchen:

Empty tins with
plastic lids

An empty tin
rattled inside
makes a
fast, loud drum.

Make sure the tins
have no sharp edges.

Empty yoghurt pots
make a clip-clop sound
on a table.

Stevie still wanted
to play the trumpet.
Mummy showed him
how to make a better
trumpet-noise with
a comb and paper.

Put a piece of
tissue-paper over
a clean comb.
Hold the paper
against your
lips and hum.

It tickles.

Baby Robin Rupert liked the music now it
was not too loud. He joined in with his
rattle. Mummy and Tim made grown-up rattles,
called 'maraccas', for the band.

HOW TO MAKE MARACCAS:

Put a big spoonful
of dry rice into a
dry, empty yoghurt
carton. Fix another
yoghurt carton to it,
tightly and firmly,
with sellotape.

Make sure it *is* firm, or . . .

Shake it.

Dad came home.
He liked Topsy and
Tim's music.

"Come to my shed," said Dad.
"I'll show you some more ideas."

Dad showed Topsy
and Tim how to
make music with
a long piece of
wood, and then
with scratchy
glass-paper.

Hold the wood at one end.
Tap it on an *old* table
edge. Ask Mummy first.

Tap it near your hand
for high notes. Tap the
far end for low notes.

Wrap the scratchy
glass-paper round
two blocks of wood
or boxes. Fix it with
drawing-pins or
sellotape.

Rub them together
to make a lovely
swish-swish noise.

Topsy and Tim made music with jamjars and
a jugful of water. Here is how to do it:

Pour water into eight jamjars. Fill each one a
little deeper. Tap them with a stick. Each jar
will make a different note. The deeper the water,
the lower the note. Add to the water, or pour some
away, until you have a scale of eight clear notes.
Then you can play tunes.

Stevie's junk-dangle would not play tunes
but it made nice funny noises.

TO MAKE A JUNK-DANGLE: first find some junk to
dangle. Cardboard tubes, foil pie-cases, hollow
boxes . . . all sorts of junk sounds funny when you
tap it with a stick. Hang your junk on a coat-hanger
with string or wool, making holes if need be.
Do not use anything that might break.

Topsy and Tim
tried to make
a guitar like
Dad's. It didn't
work.
They tried again
with Mummy's help,
and made one that
played nicely,
although it didn't
look like a guitar.

THEY USED

. . . another of those
plastic-lidded tins
(without the lid).

4 elastic
bands and
sellotape.

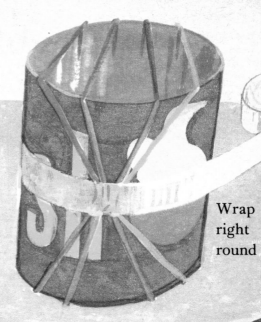

Wrap
right
round

They stretched the
elastic bands over
the tin, like this.

Then they gathered the
middles together
on both sides. They
fixed them in
place with
sellotape.

The bands over
the open top
played sweetly.
On the bottom
they made
a tinny
noise.

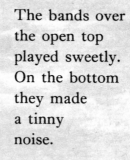

Mummy and Dad helped
Topsy and Tim make a
big, twangy
broomstick
bass-fiddle.

Find a big, sturdy
cardboard box. Make sure
Kitty isn't in it.
Seal it with wide,
sticky parcel-tape, and
tape two long edges.

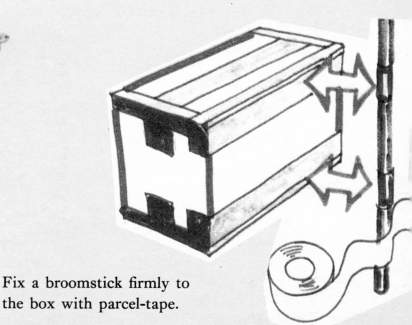

Fix a broomstick firmly to
the box with parcel-tape.

Find a long
piece of smooth
string. Coil it
tightly round
the broomstick
near the top and
fix it with parcel-tape. Stretch the
string over the box and fix it to
the bottom end of the broomstick
in the same way. Make it taut.
Find a small, strong,
rigid box and push it
under the string. If you
can't find one, a
yoghurt pot will do,
but notch it to hold
the string in
place.

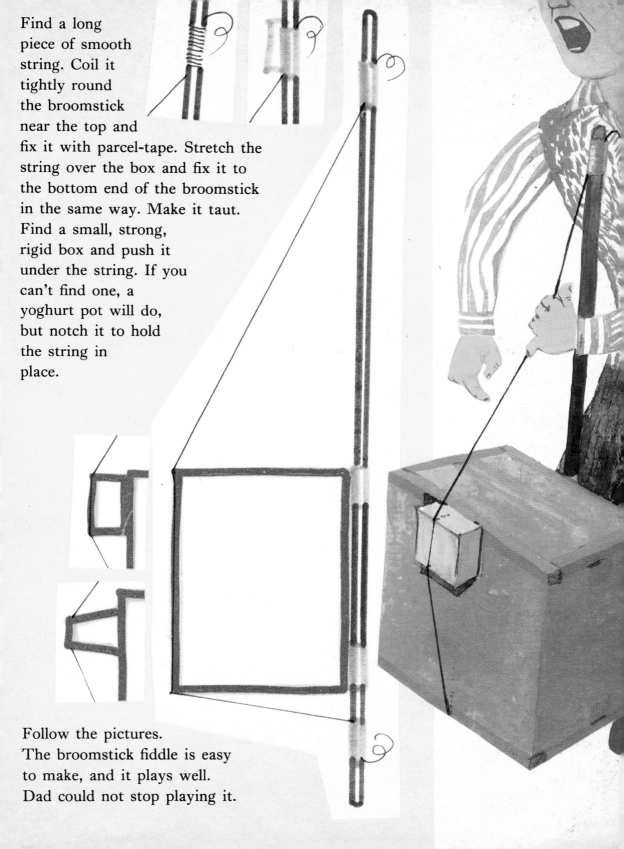

Follow the pictures.
The broomstick fiddle is easy
to make, and it plays well.
Dad could not stop playing it.

Miss Terry helped
Topsy and Tim, Tony
and Stevie to give
a concert for the
other children
at school.
It was great fun.
The children
clapped hands
for Topsy and Tim.
Then they made
their own music.
Topsy and Tim
showed them how.

Now you can make music like Topsy and Tim.